Postman Pat's
Winter

Hippo

Scholastic Children's Books,
Commonwealth House, 1-19 New Oxford Street,
London WC1A 1NU, UK
a division of Scholastic Ltd

London ~ New York ~ Toronto ~ Sydney ~ Auckland

First published by Scholastic Ltd, 1997

ISBN 0 590 19573 5

Printed in Belgium by Proost

Summer is over. It's raining as Postman
Pat and Jess the cat deliver the post.

Every day, Pat looks at the barometer. It tells him if the weather is going to change.

When winter is coming, the trees lose their leaves. On frosty days, ice forms at the edges of the pond.

In winter snow sometimes blocks the road.
Pat has to drive very carefully.

Pat wears his winter jacket to keep the cold out. He warms his hands by the fire.

Even in the snow, Pat and Jess deliver post to Greendale School.

When snow covers the houses and fields,
Greendale looks magical and exciting.

George Lancaster uses a spade to clear
the snow at Intake Farm.

George's hens keep warm inside the henhouse.

Sometimes the snow is so deep that Alf Thompson and Pat ride on a sledge to deliver letters and food to their friends.

Delivering letters on ice is dangerous. Pat falls over with a bump! Dorothy Thompson helps him up.

In winter, the days are short and it starts
to get dark before Pat has his tea.

Trucks and cars often become stuck in thick snow. Pat helps Ted Glen to dig his truck out of the snow.

Pat and Jess drive home. Greendale is an exciting place in winter!